SPIRITUAL simplicity

[**doing** less • **loving** more]

SPIRITUAL SIMPLICITY

Table of Contents

How to Start Your Own Small Group

The fact that you are even reading this page says a lot about you. It says that you are either one of those people who has to read everything, or it says you are open to God using you to lead a group.

Leading a small group can sound intimidating, but it really doesn't have to be. Think of it more as gathering a few friends to get to know each other better and to have some discussion around spiritual matters.

Here are a few practical tips to help you get started:

1. Pray — One of the most important principles of spiritual leadership is to realize you can't do this on your own. No matter how long you've been a Christian or been involved in ministry, you need the power of the Holy Spirit. Lean on Him; He will help you.

2. Invite some friends — Don't be afraid to ask people to come to your group. You will be surprised how many people are open to a study like this. Whether you have 4 or 14 in your group, it can be a powerful experience. You should probably plan on at least an hour and a half for your group meeting.

3. Get your materials — You will need to get a DVD of the video teaching done by Chip Ingram. You can get the DVD from www.livingontheedge.org. Also, it will be helpful for each person to have their own study guide. You can also purchase those through the website.

4. Be prepared to facilitate — Just a few minutes a week in preparation can make a huge difference in the group experience. Preview the video lesson, and review the discussion questions. If you don't think your group can get through all the questions, select the ones that are most relevant to your group.

6. Learn to say "I don't know" — When tough questions come up, it's ok for you to say "I don't know." Take the pressure off. No one expects you to have all the answers.

7. Love your group — Maybe the most important thing you bring to the group is your personal care for them. If you will pray for them, encourage them, call them, e-mail them, involve them, and love them, God will be pleased and you will have a lot of fun along the way.

Thank you for your availability. May God bless you as you serve Him by serving others.

How to Get the Most Out of This Experience

This small group study is for people who are tired, overextended, and maxed out. And it seems that those words describe most everyone these days. In order to get the most out of this study, you'll have to make the decision to dive in and engage this material.

Listed below are the segments you'll experience each week as well as some hints for getting the most out of this experience. If you are leading the group, you'll find some additional help and coaching on pages 73.

1. Watch the Video

It is important for us to get "before God" and submit ourselves to his truth. During this section you will watch the video teaching by Chip.

A teaching outline with fill-ins is provided for each session. As you follow along, write down questions or insights that you can share during the discussion time.

Even though most of the verses will appear on the screen and in your notes, it's a great idea to bring your own Bible each week. It will allow you to make notes in your own Bible and find other passages that might be relevant to that week's study.

2. Talk It Over

We not only grow by listening to God's word, but we grow "in community." The friendship and insights of those in the group will enrich your small group experience. Several discussion questions are provided for your group to further engage the teaching content. Keep the following guidelines in mind for having a healthy group discussion.

- **Be involved.** Jump in and share your thoughts. Your ideas are important and you have a perspective that is unique and can benefit the other group members.
- **Be a good listener.** Value what others are sharing. Seek to really understand the perspective of others in your group and don't be afraid to ask follow up questions.
- **Be courteous.** Spirited discussion is great. Disrespect and personal attacks are not. When there is disagreement, focus on the issue and never turn the discussion into a personal attack.
- **Be focused.** Stay on topic. Help the group explore the subject at hand and try to save unrelated questions or stories for afterwards.

- **Be careful not to dominate.** Be aware of the amount of talking you are doing in proportion to the rest of the group and make space for others to speak.
- **Be a learner.** Stay sensitive to what God might be wanting to teach you through the lesson, as well as through what others have to say. Focus more on your own growth rather than making a point or winning an argument.

3. Live It Out

"Bio" is a word that is synonymous with "life". Found in the three simple letters B.I.O. is the key to helping you become the person God wants you to be.

B = COME **"BEFORE GOD"** DAILY

Meet with Him personally – through His word and prayer – to enjoy His presence, receive His direction, and follow His will.

I = DO LIFE **"IN COMMUNITY"** WEEKLY

Structure your week to personally connect in safe relationships that provide love, support, transparency, challenge, and accountability.

O = BE **"ON MISSION"** 24/7

Cultivate a mindset to live out Jesus' love for others through acts of sacrifice and service at home, work, play, and church.

4. ACCELERATE *20 minutes that turn concepts into convictions*

Inspiration comes from hearing God's Word; **motivation** grows by discussing God's Word; **transformation** occurs when you study it for yourself.

If you want to "accelerate" your growth, here is an assignment you can do at home each week. Our convictions become even stronger when we dig into Scripture and discover truth for ourselves. To help you get the most out of this exercise, consider partnering up with somebody in your group who will also commit to do the assignment this week. Then, after you have each done the assignment, agree to spend 10-15 minutes in person or by phone to share what you learned and are applying.

SESSION one

[All You Need Is Love]

Take It In

The Silicon Valley Shuffle

(4 words define the dance)

Our desires to "do it all", "be it all", and "have it all" produces ______________________________.

The resulting complexity produces a life that:

- Moves too fast
- Delivers too little
- Demands too much

The symptoms of a complex life

- Fatigue is high
- Margin is thin
- Relationships are shallow
- Families are fractured
- Marriages drift
- Kids are neglected
- Deep, authentic relationships are absent

Is the good swallowing up the ______________________________?

Is it really possible to break out of this high pace, high demand, guilt-producing disease and simplify your life?

Two Diagnostic Questions

1. What do you want to be ______________________ for?

   ____

   ____

   ____

2. If you had to choose ______________________ word to be associated with your name, what word would you choose?

   ____

   ____

   ____

The Bible says the word we should be known for is ______________________.

> *If I speak in the tongues of men and of angels, but have not love, I am only a resounding gong or a clanging cymbal. If I have the gift of prophecy and can fathom all mysteries and all knowledge, and if I have a faith that can move mountains, but have not love, I am nothing. If I give all I possess to the poor and surrender my body to the flames, but have not love, I gain nothing.*
>
> **1 CORINTHIANS 13:1–3 (NIV)**

> *There is a way that seems right to a man, but in the end it leads to death.*
>
> **PROVERBS 14:12 (NIV)**

The key to Spiritual Simplicity is ______________________.

Talk It Over

1. To what degree are you doing the Silicon Valley Shuffle? How much is it impacting your life?

2. Over the last 25–30 years, what are some things that have come along that have made our lives more complex?

3. Chip listed seven symptoms of a complex life. Share a symptom of your complex life. It might be one of the ones Chip listed, or it might be something different.

4. Chip shared a couple of questions that get at the core of what drives us. One of those questions was, "What do you want to be known for?" If someone had been watching how you lived your life the last 5 years, what would they say you wanted to be known for?

Live It Out – B.I.O.

"Bio" is a word that is synonymous with "life". Found in those three simple letters B.I.O. is the key to helping you become the person God wants you to be.

B = COME "BEFORE GOD" DAILY

Meet with Him personally – through His word and prayer – to enjoy His presence, receive His direction, and follow His will.

I = DO LIFE "IN COMMUNITY" WEEKLY

Structure your week to personally connect in safe relationships that provide love, support, transparency, challenge, and accountability.

O = BE "ON MISSION" 24/7

Cultivate a mindset to live out Jesus' love for others through acts of sacrifice and service at home, work, play, and church.

Come Before God

5. Read 1 Corinthians 13:1–3 out loud to the group from a couple of different translations. What stands out to you most from this passage?

To be more loving and to simplify your life, what do you sense God might want you to change?

Do Life In Community

6. What are some practical ways that you could encourage and challenge one another when it comes to living the complex life of the Silicon Valley Shuffle?

Be On Mission

7. How could simplifying your life help you be more "missional" in your everyday life?

Accelerate *20 minutes that turns concepts into convictions*

Inspiration comes from hearing God's Word; **motivation** grows by discussing God's Word; **transformation** occurs when you study it for yourself.

If you want to "accelerate" your growth, here is an assignment you can do this week. To help you get the most out of this exercise, consider partnering up with somebody in your group who will also commit to do the assignment this week. Then, after you have each done the assignment, agree to spend 10 minutes by phone to share what you learned and what you are applying.

Come Before God

1. Read the following passage carefully and slowly:

Dear friends, let us love one another, for love comes from God. Everyone who loves has been born of God and knows God. Whoever does not love does not know God, because God is love. This is how God showed his love among us: He sent his one and only Son into the world that we might live through him. This is love: not that we loved God, but that he loved us and sent his Son as an atoning sacrifice for our sins. Dear friends, since God so loved us, we also ought to love one another.

And so we know and rely on the love God has for us.

God is love. Whoever lives in love lives in God, and God in him. In this way, love is made complete among us so that we will have confidence on the day of judgment, because in this world we are like him. There is no fear in love. But perfect love drives out fear, because fear has to do with punishment. The one who fears is not made perfect in love.

We love because he first loved us. If anyone says, "I love God," yet hates his brother, he is a liar. For anyone who does not love his brother, whom he has seen, cannot love God, whom he has not seen. And he has given us this command: Whoever loves God must also love his brother.

1 JOHN 4:7–11,16–21 (NIV)

2. Make a list of statements from this passage that describe God's love for us.

    - He sent his one and only Son into the world.
    -
    -
    -
    -
    -

3. Go through this passage and underline all the statements that make a connection between God's love for us and our ability to love other people.

4. Verse 18 says, "There is no fear in love. But perfect love drives out fear, because fear has to do with punishment. The one who fears is not made perfect in love."

    How does perfect love drive out fear?

    ____

    ____

    ____

Do Life In Community

5. Get together with a Christian friend this week or plan a 15-minute phone call, and discuss the following 2 questions:

    - What are the biggest barriers in your life to being more loving?
    - What is your next step in simplifying your life so that you can live a life of love?

Be On Mission

6. You miss opportunities to love when you are always in a hurry. This week make it your goal to ______________________________ slow down. Walk slower, drive slower, and take time for the people in your life.

SESSION two

[What's Love Got To Do With It?]

Take It In

What's love got to do with Spiritual Simplicity? ________________________________!!!

To really understand Spiritual Simplicity, you need to be able to unpack

____________________________.

1 Corinthians 13 was written as a ____________________________.

> *If I speak in the tongues of men and of angels, but have not love, I am only a resounding gong or a clanging cymbal. If I have the gift of prophecy and can fathom all mysteries and all knowledge, and if I have a faith that can move mountains, but have not love, I am nothing. If I give all I possess to the poor and surrender my body to the flames, but have not love, I gain nothing.*
>
> 1 CORINTHIANS 13:1–3 (NIV)

The Overarching Principle

Anything - love = ____________________________

Love's Supremacy

1. ____________________________ without love produces nothing.
2. ____________________________ without love leads to becoming nothing.
3. ____________________________ without love profits nothing.

Three Keys to Simplifying Your Life

1. The secret to simplifying your life is ______________________.
2. You can only do less when you ______________________ to love more.
3. You have to begin to redefine ______________________.

Unconscious questions we ask

How did I do? Performance

What do I have? Possessions

How much do I give? Provision

Three new questions to consciously ask

Who am I ______________________? A question about character

How am I ______________________ it? A question about stewardship

______________________ do I give it? A question about motives

Talk It Over

1. In what ways have you tried to simplify your life? What were the results?

2. What are some of the negative residual effects of a performance mentality? How much has being driven and having a focus on performance been a struggle in your life?

3. Chip said that materialism is rooted in a belief system that if we just had a little more, we would be satisfied. How can materialism complicate our lives? What are some practical ways you can combat materialism in yourself and in your family?

4. Chip said the secret to simplifying your life is focus. But it is easy for life to get busy and for us to lose our focus. As you assess your life today, how well are you doing at living a life that is focused? What helps you keep your life in focus?

Live It Out – B.I.O.

"Bio" is a word that is synonymous with "life". Found in those three simple letters B.I.O. is the key to helping you become the person God wants you to be.

B = COME "BEFORE GOD" DAILY

Meet with Him personally – through His word and prayer – to enjoy His presence, receive His direction, and follow His will.

I = DO LIFE "IN COMMUNITY" WEEKLY

Structure your week to personally connect in safe relationships that provide love, support, transparency, challenge, and accountability.

O = BE "ON MISSION" 24/7

Cultivate a mindset to live out Jesus' love for others through acts of sacrifice and service at home, work, play, and church.

Come Before God

5. How does coming before God daily and spending time with Him help keep your life in focus? How are you doing at consistently spending time alone with God?

Do Life In Community

6. How could the people in this group support you and help you to live a life of focus?

Be On Mission

7. What is one relationship or area of your life where you could be more loving? What practical step will you take?

Inspiration comes from hearing God's Word; **motivation** grows by discussing God's Word; **transformation** occurs when you study it for yourself.

If you want to "accelerate" your growth, here is an assignment you can do this week. To help you get the most out of this exercise, consider partnering up with somebody in your group who will also commit to do the assignment this week. Then, after you have each done the assignment, agree to spend 10 minutes by phone to share what you learned and what you are applying.

Come Before God

1. Read the following passage carefully and slowly:

> *[34]Hearing that Jesus had silenced the Sadducees, the Pharisees got together. [35]One of them, an expert in the law, tested him with this question: [36]"Teacher, which is the greatest commandment in the Law?"*
>
> *[37]Jesus replied: "'Love the Lord your God with all your heart and with all your soul and with all your mind.' [38]This is the first and greatest commandment. [39]And the second is like it: 'Love your neighbor as yourself.' [40]All the Law and the Prophets hang on these two commandments."*
>
> MATTHEW 22:34–40 (NIV)

2. Do you think the Pharisees would have been surprised by Jesus' answer to the questions in verse 36? Why or why not?

3. What does Jesus mean when he says, "all the Law and the Prophets hang on these two statements"?

4. Why is this passage significant in a discussion about love being the key to spiritual simplicity?

Do Life In Community

5. This week, memorize Matthew 22:36–39. Find a friend or someone in your small group who will also memorize this passage with you in the coming week.

Be On Mission

6. This week, what is one practical way that you will apply the challenge of Jesus in Matthew 22:39 to "love your neighbor as yourself"?

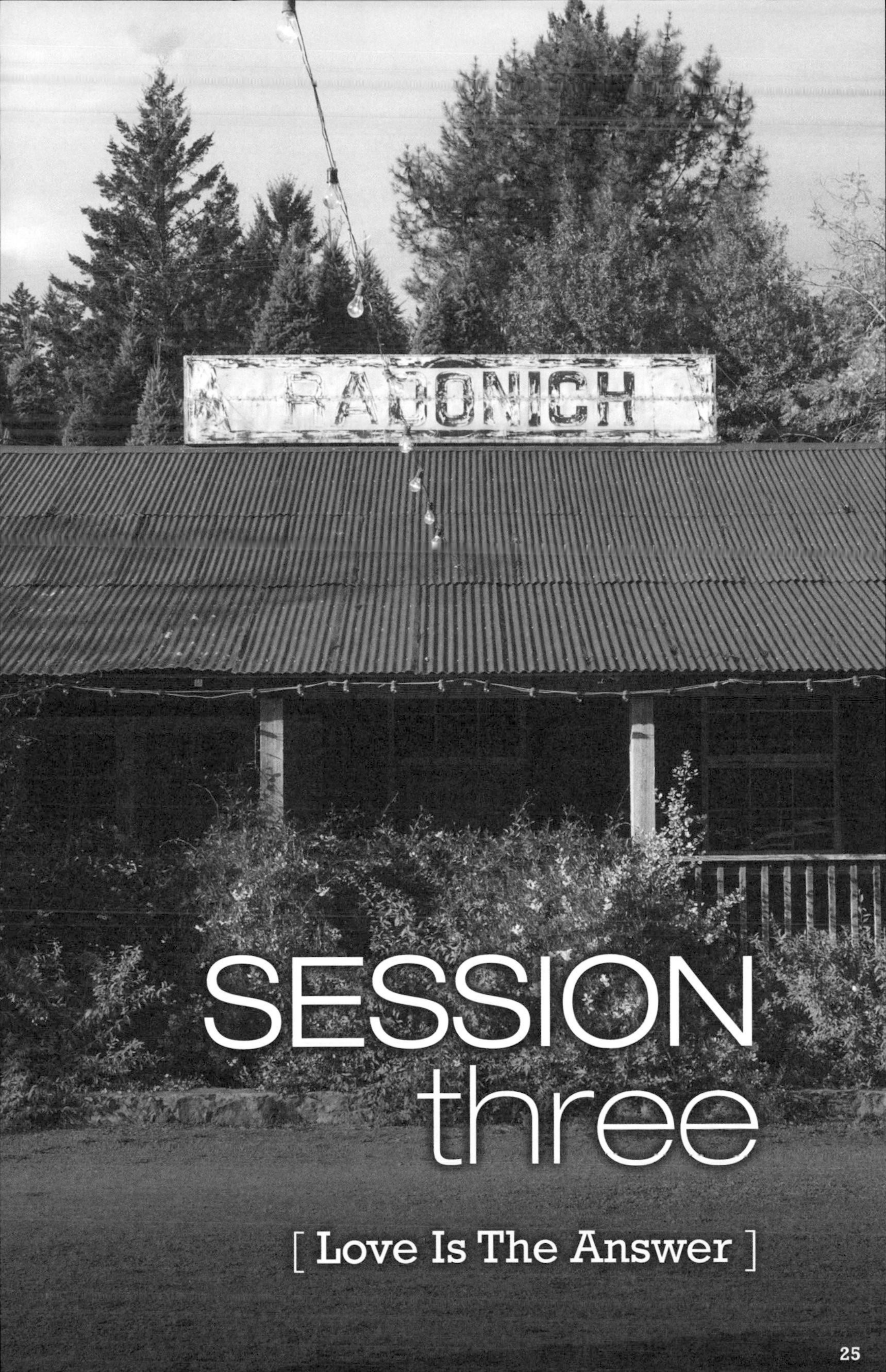

SESSION three

[Love Is The Answer]

Take It In

Three Ways Love Simplifies Your Life

Love provides ______________________________.

Love frames your ______________________________.

Love diffuses ______________________________.

The important becomes trivial and the trivial becomes important when love is minimized and trivia is maximized.

What Does It Mean To Love?

Love is giving another person what they need the most, when they deserve it the least, at great personal cost by the power of the Holy Spirit living in you.

How Does Love Respond to Hurts?

- Truth —

Love is patient, love is kind.

1 CORINTHIANS 13:4A (NIV)

Love is patient = love has a long fuse

- Practice — When you are wounded, you ______________________________ the blow (pillow) and you give them a ______________________________ (kindness).

Talk It Over

1. Is there any wound or bitterness in your life that is robbing you of spiritual simplicity? If so, share that with the group. If you aren't currently dealing with a hurt, share a time from your past that you had to deal with bitterness and what you did to resolve it.

2. Chip said "Love is giving another person what they need the most, when they deserve it the least, at great personal cost by the power of the Holy Spirit living in you." What most strikes you about that definition? How is Chip's definition different from the world's view of love?

3. Patience in love means "absorbing the blow". What are some biblical, historical, or contemporary examples of someone "absorbing the blow" when they were wronged?

4. What does it look like in your life to absorb the blow?

Live It Out – B.I.O.

"Bio" is a word that is synonymous with "life". Found in those three simple letters B.I.O. is the key to helping you become the person God wants you to be.

B = COME "BEFORE GOD" DAILY

Meet with Him personally – through His word and prayer – to enjoy His presence, receive His direction, and follow His will.

I = DO LIFE "IN COMMUNITY" WEEKLY

Structure your week to personally connect in safe relationships that provide love, support, transparency, challenge, and accountability.

O = BE "ON MISSION" 24/7

Cultivate a mindset to live out Jesus' love for others through acts of sacrifice and service at home, work, play, and church.

Come Before God

5. Chip said showing kindness in love means doing something generous for the other person. Jesus said,

> *But I tell you who hear me: Love your enemies, do good to those who hate you, bless those who curse you, pray for those who mistreat you.*
>
> LUKE 6:27–28 (NIV)

Is there somebody you are having trouble with that you need to bless and "do good to"? What is the next step that you will take?

Do Life In Community

6. How can this group support you and hold you accountable to being more patient and kind?

Be On Mission

7. Think of someone you know that isn't a Christian. How could you show them the love of Jesus through patience and kindness? Be specific.

Accelerate *20 minutes that turns concepts into convictions*

Inspiration comes from hearing God's Word; **motivation** grows by discussing God's Word; **transformation** occurs when you study it for yourself.

If you want to "accelerate" your growth, here is an assignment you can do this week. To help you get the most out of this exercise, consider partnering up with somebody in your group who will also commit to do the assignment this week. Then, after you have each done the assignment, agree to spend 10 minutes by phone to share what you learned and what you are applying.

Come Before God

1. Read the following passage carefully and slowly:

> *[12]Therefore, as God's chosen people, holy and dearly loved, clothe yourselves with compassion, kindness, humility, gentleness and patience. [13]Bear with each other and forgive whatever grievances you may have against one another. Forgive as the Lord forgave you. [14]And over all these virtues put on love, which binds them all together in perfect unity.*
>
> *[15]Let the peace of Christ rule in your hearts, since as members of one body you were called to peace. And be thankful.*
>
> COLOSSIANS 3:12–15 (NIV)

2. How does being "God's chosen people, holy and dearly loved" help us clothe ourselves with the qualities listed in verse 12?

3. Think for a moment about how you get dressed each morning. In verse 12, why is getting dressed ("clothe yourselves") a good word picture for the point Paul is making in this verse?

4. Why do you think Paul ends verse 15 with the challenge to "be thankful"? How is gratitude significant when it comes to responding to those who have hurt us?

Do Life In Community

5. Get together with a Christian friend this week or plan a 15-minute phone call to discuss Colossians 3:12 where Paul said to, "clothe yourselves with compassion, kindness, humility, gentleness and patience". What are the barriers in your life that keep you from reflecting these qualities? How can you support and help each other in pursuing these qualities?

6. Read the following words of Jesus:

You have heard that it was said, 'Love your neighbor and hate your enemy.' But I tell you: Love your enemies and pray for those who persecute you, that you may be sons of your Father in heaven. He causes his sun to rise on the evil and the good, and sends rain on the righteous and the unrighteous. If you love those who love you, what reward will you get? Are not even the tax collectors doing that? And if you greet only your brothers, what are you doing more than others? Do not even pagans do that? Be perfect, therefore, as your heavenly Father is perfect.

MATTHEW 5:43–48 (NIV)

Who is the most difficult person for you to love? Stop right now and pray for them, and then commit to one tangible act of love toward them in this next week.

SESSION four

[Love Me Tender]

Take It In

How Does Love Respond to Differences?

Truth —

> *...It does not envy, it does not boast, it is not proud. It is not rude, it is not self-seeking, it is not easily angered, it keeps no record of wrongs.*
>
> 1 CORINTHIANS 13:4B–5 (NIV)

Practice — Love chooses to ________________________________ differences and refuses to compare.

The Context — The two responses that are prohibited in this passage are

________________________________ and ________________________________.

The Principle — Comparison always leads to carnality.

- Envy compares ________________________________ and produces jealousy, anger, resentment, and bitterness.
- Arrogance compares ________________________________ and produces pride, boasting, rudeness, and independence.

Envy compares and says, "I don't matter very much."

Arrogance compares and says, "You don't matter very much."

- The envious must believe that God is ________________________________ and has sovereignly and wisely given them what's best and will fulfill his purposes.

For the LORD God is a sun and shield; The LORD gives grace and glory; No good thing does He withhold from those who walk uprightly.

PSALM 84:11 (NASB)

Humility is the prerequisite for grace.

Talk It Over

1. When you were a kid growing up, did you struggle with lack of self-esteem? Were you the "golden child" who maybe had too much self-esteem? In those earlier years, where would you put yourself on the continuum from too little self-esteem to too much self-esteem?

2. Chip said that envy can cause us to get make bad choices, all in the name of getting ahead, providing for our kids, or keeping up appearances. How much is envy an issue for you? How can you keep from being sucked into the world's pursuit of "more"?

3. Chip said "when you compare, you're going to be unloving". How is it unloving to compare ourselves (either upwards or downwards) to others?

4. Love chooses to celebrate differences and refuses to compare. Take a few moments to celebrate the differences within your group. Share what you appreciate as strengths of others in the group that you don't possess.

Live It Out – B.I.O.

"Bio" is a word that is synonymous with "life". Found in those three simple letters B.I.O. is the key to helping you become the person God wants you to be.

B = COME "BEFORE GOD" DAILY

Meet with Him personally – through His word and prayer – to enjoy His presence, receive His direction, and follow His will.

I = DO LIFE "IN COMMUNITY" WEEKLY

Structure your week to personally connect in safe relationships that provide love, support, transparency, challenge, and accountability.

O = BE "ON MISSION" 24/7

Cultivate a mindset to live out Jesus' love for others through acts of sacrifice and service at home, work, play, and church.

Come Before God

5. Psalm 84:11 (NASB) says, "For the LORD God is a sun and shield;

The LORD gives grace and glory; No good thing does He withhold from those who walk uprightly."

PSALM 84:11 (NASB)

How does gratitude and the goodness of God help with in the struggle with envy and arrogance?

Do Life In Community

6. If we struggle with pride, it can lead to a spirit of independence and a lack of accountability. To counteract that, we need to work at letting people into our lives. How well are you doing at letting people into your life and being accountable? What are the barriers to letting people in?

Be On Mission

7. Chip said that pride will lead to insensitivity. What are some practical ways that you can be more sensitive to those around you? How can you keep from judging or looking down on people?

Accelerate *20 minutes that turns concepts into convictions*

Inspiration comes from hearing God's Word; **motivation** grows by discussing God's Word; **transformation** occurs when you study it for yourself.

If you want to "accelerate" your growth, here is an assignment you can do this week. To help you get the most out of this exercise, consider partnering up with somebody in your group who will also commit to do the assignment this week. Then, after you have each done the assignment, agree to spend 10 minutes by phone to share what you learned and what you are applying.

Come Before God

1. Read the following passage carefully and slowly. Then consider reading it in another translation.

> *But godliness with contentment is great gain. For we brought nothing into the world, and we can take nothing out of it. But if we have food and clothing, we will be content with that. People who want to get rich fall into temptation and a trap and into many foolish and harmful desires that plunge men into ruin and destruction. For the love of money is a root of all kinds of evil. Some people, eager for money, have wandered from the faith and pierced themselves with many griefs.*
>
> 1 TIMOTHY 6:6–10 (NIV)

2. The antidote to envy is contentment and gratitude. What are some principles from this passage that are helpful in learning to be content and grateful?

    -
    -
    -
    -

3. Paul says that some who are "eager for money, have wandered from the faith". How can envy and the pursuit of more cause you to wander from the faith?

4. Spend a few minutes Journaling. Write down what you are grateful for. Finish your journaling time by writing out what you sense God is saying to you.

Do Life In Community

5. Get together with a Christian friend this week or plan a 15-minute phone call, and have a candid discussion about envy and arrogance. Take an honest look at your attitudes, and share where you are most apt to struggle with envy and arrogance. Then pray with and for one another.

6. As you go through your week, make it a point to celebrate differences. Rather than seeing differences as an irritation, see them as a point of celebration. Work at engaging and loving people who are different than you.

SESSION five

[Looking For Love In All The Wrong Places]

Take It In

Review from Session 4

Situation #1 — How does love respond to hurts?

- The truth —

> *"Love is patient, love is kind"*
>
> 1 CORINTHIANS 13:4A (NIV)

- The practice — When you are hurt, wounded, rejected, or ignored, love "absorbs" the blows (pillow) and returns a "hug" (kindness).

Situation #2 — How does love respond to differences?

- The truth —

> *...love does not envy, it does not boast, it is not rude, it is not self-seeking, it is not easily angered, it keeps no record of wrongs.*
>
> 1 CORINTHIANS 13:4B–5 (NIV)

- The practice — Love celebrates our differences. Love refuses to compare upwards (envy) or downwards (arrogance). (1 Corinthians 12:12–31 (NIV))

Situation #3 — How Does Love Respond to Failure?

- The truth —

Love does not delight in evil but rejoices with the truth. It always protects, always trusts, always hopes, always perseveres. Love never fails.

1 CORINTHIANS 13:6–8A (NIV)

- The practice — Love responds to failure with ______________________ and ______________________. Truthful and grace-filled love chooses to bear, believe, hope, and endure all things.

Truth – Love = Judgment

Grace – Truth = Sentimentalism

How Do Truth and Grace Go Together?

1. Love ______________________ all things.
    - True love covers over and protects.
    - True love refuses to ______________________ the failures of others.

2. Love ______________________ all things.
    - True love believes the best of another person.
    - True love says, "______________________".

3. Love ______________________ all things.

- The word "hope" occurs 32 times in the New Testament. It has in it the idea of a hope that results in a deliverance.
- Biblical hope is in the anchor and promise of

  ______________________________.

4. Love ______________________ all things

- The word "endure" contains the idea of living under the strain of a weight.
- True love won't give up, quit, or leave.

Talk It Over

1. Where have you failed in the past and, in your failure, ended up finding God's love?

2. True love covers over, protects, and refuses to exploit. Can you think of a time when someone did that for you? Share that experience with the group.

3. Chip said simplicity begins with allowing God's love to get deep into our own hearts. How does accepting God's unconditional love simplify our lives?

4. Chip said "don't confuse endurance with codependency". What would be the signs that someone has moved from enduring love to codependency?

Live It Out – B.I.O.

"Bio" is a word that is synonymous with "life". Found in those three simple letters B.I.O. is the key to helping you become the person God wants you to be.

B = COME **"BEFORE GOD"** DAILY

Meet with Him personally – through His word and prayer – to enjoy His presence, receive His direction, and follow His will.

I = DO LIFE **"IN COMMUNITY"** WEEKLY

Structure your week to personally connect in safe relationships that provide love, support, transparency, challenge, and accountability.

O = BE **"ON MISSION"** 24/7

Cultivate a mindset to live out Jesus' love for others through acts of sacrifice and service at home, work, play, and church.

Come Before God

5. Read Romans 15:4 and 15:13. What do these verses teach us about biblical hope?

Do Life In Community

6. Is your natural tendency to show up stronger with "truth" or with "grace"? What are some of the barriers that keep small groups from modeling truth and grace?

Be On Mission

7. Who in your life needs to hear the words, "I believe in you and I'm for you"?

Accelerate *20 minutes that turns concepts into convictions*

Inspiration comes from hearing God's Word; **motivation** grows by discussing God's Word; **transformation** occurs when you study it for yourself.

If you want to "accelerate" your growth, here is an assignment you can do this week. To help you get the most out of this exercise, consider partnering up with somebody in your group who will also commit to do the assignment this week. Then, after you have each done the assignment, agree to spend 10 minutes by phone to share what you learned and what you are applying.

Come Before God

1. Read John 4:4–30, which records the encounter between Jesus and the Samaritan woman. This account gives us a good picture of how Jesus modeled both truth and grace.

2. Go back through this passage and make a list of the times in the passage that Jesus showed or spoke grace to the Samaritan woman.

3. Go back through this passage, and make a list of the times in the story where Jesus spoke truth to this woman.

4. Go back through the passage one more time, and make a list of the potential barriers to Jesus showing love to this woman. For example, in verse 6 it says Jesus was tired when he arrived at the well. When we are fatigued, we often miss the opportunity to show love.

Do Life In Community

5. In the group discussion this week, the final question asked was, "Who is it in your life that needs to hear the words 'I believe in you and I'm for you'?"

   Write their name here, and make a plan to reach out to that person this week.

6. Proverbs 17:9 (NIV) says,

He who covers over an offense promotes love, but whoever repeats the matter separates close friends.

PROVERBS 17:9 (NIV)

Is there someone you know that is living under the burden of a failure? Consider reaching out to them to make sure they know that they are unconditionally loved by God and by you.

SESSION six

[In The Name Of Love]

Take It In

How can so many good things end up with ______________________ outcomes?

> *Love never fails. But where there are prophecies, they will cease; where there are tongues, they will be stilled; where there is knowledge, it will pass away. For we know in part and we prophesy in part, but when perfection comes, the imperfect disappears. When I was a child, I talked like a child, I thought like a child, I reasoned like a child. When I became a man, I put childish ways behind me. Now we see but a poor reflection as in a mirror; then we shall see face to face. Now I know in part; then I shall know fully, even as I am fully known. And now these three remain: faith, hope and love. But the greatest of these is love.*
>
> 1 CORINTHIANS 13:8–13 (NIV)

How Does Love Respond to Misplaced Priorities?

- The Practice — We have to ______________________________________ not allow the temporal good things to crowd out the eternal best things.
- The Thesis — Love is _____________________________. Love is our #1 priority.
- The Reason — Because love ________________________.

The world wants to squeeze you into its mold. You will have to take ____________________ ________________________ for your priorities to be where they need to be.

Where are your priorities right now in:

- Your relationship with your heavenly father?
- Doing life in community?
- Having a mission? Are you doing what God wants you to do?

Change will not occur by ______________________________ your schedule.

The Solution — You have to ______________________________.

- Grow up in your talking.
- Grow up in your thinking.
- Grow up in your reasoning.

The Principle

- Cloudy vision leads to ____________________________
- Clear vision leads to ________________________

Talk It Over

1. What spoke to you most from this session?

____

____

____

2. In what ways have some "good" activities kept you and those you love from the best investment of your life and energy?

____

____

____

3. What do you need to change in order to address misplaced priorities? In light of your answer, what is your next step?

4. Chip said, "cloudy vision leads to complexity". How is that true? He also said, "clear vision leads to love". How is that true?

Live It Out – B.I.O.

"Bio" is a word that is synonymous with "life". Found in those three simple letters B.I.O. is the key to helping you become the person God wants you to be.

B = COME "BEFORE GOD" DAILY

Meet with Him personally – through His word and prayer – to enjoy His presence, receive His direction, and follow His will.

I = DO LIFE "IN COMMUNITY" WEEKLY

Structure your week to personally connect in safe relationships that provide love, support, transparency, challenge, and accountability.

O = BE "ON MISSION" 24/7

Cultivate a mindset to live out Jesus' love for others through acts of sacrifice and service at home, work, play, and church.

Come Before God

5. One of the ways for us to have a clear vision for our life is to come before God on a daily basis. Share with the group about your time alone with God. What has been helpful and what are some of the barriers?

Do Life In Community

6. Take a few minutes to honestly assess how your small group is doing at building true community. What steps could you take to deepen the authenticity of relationships within your group?

Be On Mission

7. To live out God's priorities for your life, you need to be "on mission". How do you feel God has gifted you to serve Him?

Accelerate *20 minutes that turns concepts into convictions*

Inspiration comes from hearing God's Word; **motivation** grows by discussing God's Word; **transformation** occurs when you study it for yourself.

If you want to "accelerate" your growth, here is an assignment you can do this week. To help you get the most out of this exercise, consider partnering up with somebody in your group who will also commit to do the assignment this week. Then, after you have each done the assignment, agree to spend 10 minutes by phone to share what you learned and what you are applying.

Come Before God

1. Read the following passage carefully and slowly:

> *[5]I was circumcised when I was eight days old. I am a pure-blooded citizen of Israel and a member of the tribe of Benjamin—a real Hebrew if there ever was one! I was a member of the Pharisees, who demand the strictest obedience to the Jewish law. [6]I was so zealous that I harshly persecuted the church. And as for righteousness, I obeyed the law without fault.*
>
> *[7]I once thought these things were valuable, but now I consider them worthless because of what Christ has done. [8]Yes, everything else is worthless when compared with the infinite value of knowing Christ Jesus my Lord. For his sake I have discarded everything else, counting it all as garbage, so that I could gain Christ*
>
> PHILIPPIANS 3:5–8 (NLT)

2. In verses 5–6, what were Paul's priorities and where did he find his identity?

    - Religious ritual (v.5)
    -
    -
    -
    -

3. Why did Christ's death make Paul view all of his past credentials as "worthless"? What does this have to do with living a life of focused priority?

4. Paul says in Philippians 3:12–14 (NLT),

I don't mean to say that I have already achieved these things or that I have already reached perfection. But I press on to possess that perfection for which Christ Jesus first possessed me. No, dear brothers and sisters, I have not achieved it, but I focus on this one thing: Forgetting the past and looking forward to what lies ahead, I press on to reach the end of the race and receive the heavenly prize for which God, through Christ Jesus, is calling us.

PHILIPPIANS 3:12-14 (NLT)

Go through these 3 verses and circle any word or phrase that speaks to intentional living and focused priority.

Do Life In Community

5. Get together with a Christian friend this week or plan a 15-minute phone call to discuss the following questions:

    - What do you say is a priority to you that is not getting focused attention in your life right now?
    - What would it take for you to live with a clearer vision for your life?

Be On Mission

6. In the space below, write out what it is that you feel passionate about and gifted to do in serving God. Be as specific as possible.

7. What might you need to stop doing so that you can make room to be "on mission" for God?

SESSION seven

[What The World Needs Now]

Take It In

Psuedo-Love Substitutes

- Affirmation from success
- Adulation from fame
- Temporary intimacy from sex
- Attention we get from our appearance or possessions
- Esteem we receive from our position
- Security we perceive in our wealth

Our quest to be loved personally and deeply creates fast-paced, over-extended, complex lives driven to obtain success, fame, sex, looks, position, power, and wealth in a desperate hope that we will be ____________________... just for who we are!

Three Questions About Love We Must Answer

- Where do you find it?
- How do you get it?
- How do you give it away?

1. ____________________ do you find love?

Dear friends, let us love one another, for love comes from God. Everyone who loves has been born of God and knows God. Whoever does not love does not know God, because God is love.

1 JOHN 4:7–8 (NIV)

The LORD your God is with you, he is mighty to save. He will take great delight in you, he will quiet you with his love, he will rejoice over you with singing."

ZEPHANIAH 3:17 (NIV)

2. ____________ do you get love?

- Through our ____________ family.
- Through our ____________ family.
- Through times of ____________.

And not only this, but we also exult in our tribulations, knowing that tribulation brings about perseverance; and perseverance, proven character; and proven character, hope; and hope does not disappoint, because the love of God has been poured out within our hearts through the Holy Spirit who was given to us.

ROMANS 5:3–5 (NASB)

Sometimes the very thing we want to be taken away is a ____________ from God that allows so we can experience Him like never before.

3. How do you ____________ love away?

Jesus did a number of very ____________ things to give love away.

- He talked with people.
- He walked with people.

- He ate with people.
- He prayed with people.
- He suffered with people.
- He taught people.
- He forgave people.

Talk It Over

1. Which of those pseudo substitutes of love are you most tempted by?

2. When you were growing up, how openly was love expressed in your family?

3. How were you impacted personally by the way your family did or did not express love? How hard is it for you to openly express love?

4. Chip said "Sometimes the very thing we want to be taken away is a grace gift from God that allows so we can experience Him like never before." Share a time or experience when you found this to be true.

Live It Out – B.I.O.

"Bio" is a word that is synonymous with "life". Found in those three simple letters B.I.O. is the key to helping you become the person God wants you to be.

B = COME "BEFORE GOD" DAILY

Meet with Him personally – through His word and prayer – to enjoy His presence, receive His direction, and follow His will.

I = DO LIFE "IN COMMUNITY" WEEKLY

Structure your week to personally connect in safe relationships that provide love, support, transparency, challenge, and accountability.

O = BE "ON MISSION" 24/7

Cultivate a mindset to live out Jesus' love for others through acts of sacrifice and service at home, work, play, and church.

Come Before God

5. Zephaniah 3:17 (NIV) says,

> *The LORD your God is with you, he is mighty to save. He will take great delight in you, he will quiet you with his love, he will rejoice over you with singing.*
>
> ZEPHANIAH 3:17 (NIV)

How does this verse align with the view of God you have been carrying around? How hard is it for you to embrace that God delights in you and rejoices over you with singing?

Do Life In Community

6. Who in your family or circle of friends desperately needs to know that God loves them? In what specific ways can you express God's love to them in the coming week?

Be On Mission

7. From the list of the ways that Jesus gave love away, which one could you put into practice immediately?

Accelerate *20 minutes that turns concepts into convictions*

Inspiration comes from hearing God's Word; **motivation** grows by discussing God's Word; **transformation** occurs when you study it for yourself.

If you want to "accelerate" your growth, here is an assignment you can do this week. To help you get the most out of this exercise, consider partnering up with somebody in your group who will also commit to do the assignment this week. Then, after you have each done the assignment, agree to spend 10 minutes by phone to share what you learned and what you are applying.

Come Before God

1. Read the following passage carefully and slowly:

   Praise be to the God and Father of our Lord Jesus Christ, who has blessed us in the heavenly realms with every spiritual blessing in Christ. For he chose us in him before the creation of the world to be holy and blameless in his sight. In love he predestined us to be adopted as his sons through Jesus Christ, in accordance with his pleasure and will—to the praise of his glorious grace, which he has freely given us in the One he loves. In him we have redemption through his blood, the forgiveness of sins, in accordance with the riches of God's grace that he lavished on us with all wisdom and understanding.

   EPHESIANS 1:3–8 (NIV)

2. Go through this passage and circle all the words or phrases that are a demonstration of God's love for you.

3. Now go through this passage and notice how our spiritual blessings are directly related to our connection with Christ. Underline all the references to Christ in the passage.

4. Which of the spiritual blessings are you most grateful for today? Why?

Do Life In Community

5. This week, bless someone with Ephesians 1:3–8. Handwrite a note or send an e-mail to them with the passage, and every time you see the word "us", substitute it with their name. Then, write a short, personal note to them letting them know how much they are loved.

Be On Mission

6. Because God has lavished His love on us, we can become conduits of his love to others. Ask God whom he wants you to extravagantly love. Then DO IT!!

SESSION eight

[Love Train (Get On Board!)]

Watch the Video

When Jesus was asked, "What is the greatest commandment?" His clear answer was…

- Love the Lord your God
- Love your neighbor as yourself

How do you sustain a lifetime of love?

1. The destination of the love train — becoming like Jesus (a Romans 12 Christian)

    - ______________________________ to God (Romans 12:1)
    - ______________________________ from the world's values (Romans 12:2)
    - Sober (accurate) ______________________________ (Romans 12:3–8)
    - ______________________________ in love (Romans 12:9–13)
    - ______________________________ respond to evil with good (Romans 12:14–21)

2. The railroad tracks of the love train are B.I.O.

    - B = ______________________________ daily
    - I = ______________________________ weekly
    - O = ______________________________ 24/7

This is the path to ______________________________

3. The barriers on the love train railroad tracks

    - Your unwillingness to go ______________________________.
    - Your unwillingness to be ______________________________.
    - Your fear of ______________________________.

Talk It Over

1. Chip said that a disciple is someone that is "becoming like Jesus". In the past, if someone had asked you, "What is a disciple?" what would you have said?

2. Over the course of your life, who or what has had the most impact on your life in helping you become like Jesus?

3. The apostle Paul calls on us to be separate from the world's values. In John 17, Jesus said that we are not *of* the world but that He did send us *in to* the world. What does it mean for you personally to be in the world, but not of the world? Be specific.

4. At the end of this session, Chip mentioned three barriers on the tracks of the "love train". Which of these is most likely to be a barrier for you? Why?

Live It Out – B.I.O.

"Bio" is a word that is synonymous with "life". Found in those three simple letters B.I.O. is the key to helping you become the person God wants you to be.

B = COME **"BEFORE GOD"** DAILY

Meet with Him personally – through His word and prayer – to enjoy His presence, receive His direction, and follow His will.

I = DO LIFE **"IN COMMUNITY"** WEEKLY

Structure your week to personally connect in safe relationships that provide love, support, transparency, challenge, and accountability.

O = BE **"ON MISSION"** 24/7

Cultivate a mindset to live out Jesus' love for others through acts of sacrifice and service at home, work, play, and church.

Come Before God

5. For you personally, what does it mean to be surrendered to God ("all in")? Is there some area of your life that you are struggling to surrender to God?

Do Life In Community

6. What are the biggest barriers to you experiencing deeper relationships?

- Too busy
- Job demands
- Fear of rejection
- Fear to initiate
- Lack of intentionality
- Past hurts
- ____________________
- ____________________

Be On Mission

7. If you could do anything for God, and time and money were no obstacle, what would you attempt?

Accelerate *20 minutes that turns concepts into convictions*

Inspiration comes from hearing God's Word; **motivation** grows by discussing God's Word; **transformation** occurs when you study it for yourself.

If you want to "accelerate" your growth, here is an assignment you can do this week. To help you get the most out of this exercise, consider partnering up with somebody in your group who will also commit to do the assignment this week. Then, after you have each done the assignment, agree to spend 10 minutes by phone to share what you learned and what you are applying.

Come Before God

1. Read Romans 12 carefully and slowly. Then, read the whole chapter in a different translation.

[1]Therefore, I urge you, brothers, in view of God's mercy, to offer your bodies as living sacrifices, holy and pleasing to God—this is your spiritual act of worship. [2]Do not conform any longer to the pattern of this world, but be transformed by the renewing of your mind. Then you will be able to test and approve what God's will is—his good, pleasing and perfect will.

[3]For by the grace given me I say to every one of you: Do not think of yourself more highly than you ought, but rather think of yourself with sober judgment, in accordance with the measure of faith God has given you. [4]Just as each of us has one body with many members, and these members do not all have the same function, [5]so in Christ we who are many form one body, and each member belongs to all the others. [6]We have different gifts, according to the grace given us. If a man's gift is prophesying, let him use it in proportion to his faith. [7]If it is serving, let him serve; if it is teaching, let him teach; [8]if it is encouraging, let him encourage; if it is contributing to the needs of others, let him give generously; if it is leadership, let him govern diligently; if it is showing mercy, let him do it cheerfully.

[9]Love must be sincere. Hate what is evil; cling to what is good. [10]Be devoted to one another in brotherly love. Honor one another above yourselves. [11]Never be lacking in zeal, but keep your spiritual fervor, serving the Lord. [12]Be joyful in hope, patient in affliction, faithful in prayer.

[13]Share with God's people who are in need. Practice hospitality.

[14]Bless those who persecute you; bless and do not curse. [15]Rejoice with those who rejoice; mourn with those who mourn. [16]Live in harmony with one another. Do not be proud, but be willing to associate with people of low position. Do not be conceited.

[17]Do not repay anyone evil for evil. Be careful to do what is right in the eyes of everybody. [18]If it is possible, as far as it depends on you, live at peace with everyone. [19]Do not take revenge, my friends, but leave room for God's wrath, for it is written: "It is mine to avenge; I will repay," says the Lord. [20]On the contrary:

"If your enemy is hungry, feed him; if he is thirsty, give him something to drink. In doing this, you will heap burning coals on his head."

[21]Do not be overcome by evil, but overcome evil with good.

ROMANS 12:1–21 (NIV)

2. In verses 1–3 and 14–21, underline every time there is a positive command (something to do) and then circle every time there is a negative command (something NOT to do).

3. In verse 1, why do you think the imagery of animal sacrifices from the Old Testament is a good word picture for surrender?

4. In verses 3–8, Paul uses the analogy of the body to illustrate how we relate to one another. What truths do you see in Paul's metaphor of the body (verses 3–8) that help you NOT think more highly of yourself than you ought to?

Do Life In Community

5. Get together with a Christian friend this week or plan a 15-minute phone call to discuss Romans 12:9–13. How are you doing at living out the qualities mentioned in these verses? What command do you most need to put into practice?

Be On Mission

6. Take a few moments to reflect on this Spiritual Simplicity study. What have you learned? How has this series impacted you? What are the most important steps you can take to sustain a lifetime of love?

HELPS for facilitating your group

[Small Group Leader Resources]

Group Agreement

People come to groups with a variety of expectations. The purpose of a group agreement is simply to make sure everyone is on the same page and that we have some common expectations.

The following Group Agreement is a tool to help you discuss specific guidelines during your first meeting. Modify anything that does not work for your group, then be sure to discuss the questions in the section called Our Game Plan. This will help you to have an even greater group experience.

WE AGREE TO THE FOLLOWING PRIORITIES

- **Take the Bible Seriously** — To seek to understand and apply God's truth in the Bible.
- **Group Attendance** — To give priority to the group meeting (call if I am going to be absent or late).
- **Safe Environment** — To create a safe place where people can be heard and feel loved (no snap judgments or simple fixes).
- **Respectful Discussion** — To speak in a respectful and honoring way to our mate and others in the group.
- **Be Confidential** — To keep anything that is shared strictly confidential and within the group.
- **Spiritual Health** — To give group members permission to help me live a godly, healthy spiritual life that is pleasing to God.
- **Building Relationships** — To get to know the other members of the group and pray for them regularly.
- **Pursue B.I.O.** — To encourage and challenge each other in coming "**B**efore God," doing life together "**I**n Community" and being "**O**n Mission" 24/7.
- **Prayer** — Regularly pray with and for each other.
- **Other**

Our Game Plan

1. What day and time will we meet?

2. Where will we meet?

3. How long will we meet each week?

4. What will we do for refreshments?

5. What will we do about childcare?

Tips for Facilitating Your Group Meeting

BEFORE THE GROUP ARRIVES

1. **Be prepared.** Your personal preparation can make a huge difference in the quality of the group experience. We strongly suggest previewing both the DVD teaching by Chip Ingram and the study guide.

2. **Pray for your group members by name.** Ask God to use your time together to touch the heart of every person in your group. Expect God to challenge and change people as a result of this study.

3. **Provide refreshments.** There's nothing like food to help a group relax and connect with each other. For the first week, we suggest you prepare a snack. After that, ask other group members to bring the food so that they share in the responsibilities of the group and make a commitment to return.

4. **Relax.** Don't try to imitate someone else's style of leading a group. Lead the group in a way that fits your style and temperament. Remember that people may feel nervous showing up for a small group study, so put them at ease when they arrive. Make sure to have all the details covered prior to your group meeting. That way, you can focus on people when they arrive.

Watch the Video

1. **Get the video ready.** Each video session will be between 15 and 20 minutes in length. Go ahead and cue up the video so you can just push play when you are ready to watch the session.

2. **Have ample materials.** Before you start the video, make sure everyone has their own copy of the study guide. Encourage the group to open to this week's session and follow along with the teaching. There is an outline in the study guide with an opportunity to fill in the outline and take notes.

3. **Arrange the room.** Set up the chairs so that everyone can see the television. After watching the video, move chairs as needed to facilitate discussion.

Talk It Over

Here are some guidelines for leading the discussion time:

1. **Make this a discussion, not a lecture.** Resist the temptation to do all the talking and to answer your own questions. Don't be afraid of a few moments of silence while people formulate their answers. A good guideline is to wait for at least five seconds after asking a question.

   You also don't need to feel like you have all the answers. There is nothing wrong with simply saying, "I don't know the answer to that, but I'll see if I can find an answer this week".

2. **Encourage everyone to participate.** Don't let one person dominate, but also don't pressure quieter members to speak during the first couple of sessions. Be patient. Ask good follow-up questions, and be sensitive to delicate issues.

3. **Affirm people's participation and input.** If an answer is clearly wrong, ask, "What led you to that conclusion?" or ask what the rest of the group thinks. If a disagreement arises, don't be too quick to shut it down. The discussion can draw out important perspectives. If you can't resolve the disagreement then, offer to research it further and return to the issue next week.

   However, if someone goes on the offensive and engages in personal attacks, you will need to step in as the leader. In the midst of spirited discussion, we must also remember that there is no place for disrespect.

4. **Detour when necessary.** If an important question is raised that isn't in the study guide, take time to discuss it. Also, if someone shares something personal and emotional, take time for them. Stop and pray for them right then. Allow the Holy Spirit room to maneuver, and follow His prompting when the discussion changes direction.

5. **Subgroups.** One of the principles of small group life is "when numbers go up, sharing goes down". If you have a large group, sometimes you may want to split up into groups of 4–6 people for the discussion time. This is a great way to give everyone, especially the quieter members, a chance to share. Choose someone to guide each of the smaller groups through the discussion. This also involves others in the leadership of the group and provides an opportunity for training new leaders.

6. **Prayer.** Be sensitive to the fact that some people in your group may be uncomfortable praying out loud. As a general rule, don't call on people to pray unless you have asked them ahead of time or have heard them pray in public. But this can also be a time to help people build their confidence to pray in a group. Consider having prayer times that ask people to just say a word or sentence of thanks to God.

Live It Out

At this point in each week's session, you will engage the B.I.O. pathway. B.I.O. is a process that is designed to help Christians live like Christians. As you integrate these three vital practices into your life, it will result in spiritual momentum and help you thrive as a follower of Jesus.

B = COME "**BEFORE GOD**" DAILY

Meet with Him personally – through His Word and prayer – in order to enjoy His Presence, receive His direction, and follow His will.

I = DO LIFE "**IN COMMUNITY**" WEEKLY

Structure your week to personally connect in safe relationships that provide love, support, transparency, challenge, and accountability.

O = BE "**ON MISSION**" 24/7

Cultivate a mindset to live out Jesus' love for others through acts of sacrifice and service at home, work, play, and church.

Accelerate *20 minutes that turns concepts into convictions*

Inspiration comes from hearing God's Word; **motivation** grows by discussing God's Word; **transformation** occurs when you study it for yourself.

If you want to "accelerate" your growth, here is an assignment you can do this week. To help you get the most out of this exercise, consider partnering up with somebody in your group who will also commit to do the assignment this week. Then, after you have each done the assignment, agree to spend 10 minutes by phone to share what you learned and what you are applying.

Session Notes

Thanks for hosting this study on *Spiritual Simplicity*. This practical study based on 1 Corinthians 13 is going to challenge and bless you. Whether you are brand new at leading a small group or you're a seasoned veteran, God is going to use you. God has a long history of using ordinary people to get his work done.

These brief notes are intended to help prepare you for each week's session. By spending just a few minutes each week previewing the video and going over these session notes, you will set the stage for a great group experience. Also, make sure to pray for your group each week.

SESSION 1 — ALL YOU NEED IS LOVE

- If your group doesn't know each other well, be sure that you spend some time getting acquainted. Don't rush right into the video lesson. Remember, small groups are not just about a study or a meeting, they are about relationships.
- Be sure to write down everyone's contact information. It's a good idea to send out an e-mail after your first meeting with everybody's contact information so that the group can stay in touch. At the back of the study guide is a roster where everyone can fill in the names and contact information of the other members.
- When you are ready to start the session, be sure that each person in your group has a copy of the study guide. The small group study guide is important for people to follow along and to take notes.

- Spend a little time in this first session talking about B.I.O. These three core practices are the pathway to maturity. You will see these letters and terms throughout this curriculum. Start getting your group comfortable with the concepts of coming "before God", doing life together "in community", and being "on mission".
- Facilitate the discussion time. Sometimes Chip will ask the facilitator to lead the way by answering the first question. This allows you to lead by example. Your willingness to share openly about your life will help others feel comfortable doing the same.
- In this introductory session, Chip will introduce the primary concept that love is the key to spiritual simplicity. Much of this session will focus on our fast-paced living and how that contributes to a complex and exhausted life. You might want to share honestly your own struggle with this issue.
- Before you wrap up your group time, be sure to introduce the Accelerate exercise in the study guide. This is an assignment they can do during the week that will help turbo-charge their growth. Encourage them to find a partner in the group who they can talk to each week about the accelerate exercise.

SESSION 2 — WHAT'S LOVE GOT TO DO WITH IT?

- Why not begin your preparation by praying right now for the people in your group. You might even want to keep their names in your Bible. You may also want to ask people in your group how you can pray for them specifically.
- If somebody doesn't come back this week, be sure and follow up with them. Even if you knew they were going to miss the meeting, give them a call or shoot them an e-mail letting them know that they were missed. It would also be appropriate to have a couple of other people in the group let them know they were missed.
- If you haven't already previewed the video, do so. It will help you know how to best facilitate the group and pick the best discussion questions for your group.
- In this session, Chip will introduce 3 questions that are helpful to people in their pursuit of spiritual simplicity. He will ask the people in your group to write these questions on a 3x5 card. It would be best if you had cards at your meeting so people can follow through right away.

SESSION 3 — LOVE IS THE ANSWER

- Did anybody miss last week's session? If so, make it a priority to follow up and let them know they were missed. It just might be your care for them that keeps them connected to the group.
- Share the load. One of the ways to raise the sense of ownership within the group is to get them involved in more than coming to the meeting. Get someone to help with refreshments. Find somebody to be in charge of the prayer requests. Get someone to be in charge of any social gathering you plan. Let someone lead the discussion one night. Spread around as much of the responsibility as possible—that's good leadership.
- Think about last week's meeting for a moment. Was there anyone that didn't talk or participate? In every group, there are extroverts and introverts. There are people who like to talk and those who are quite content NOT to talk. Not everyone engages in the same way or at the same level, but try and create an environment where everyone wants to participate.
- In this session, Chip will briefly share the gospel. As he finishes sharing the gospel, he will say, "There is probably someone in the group that can explain this further". Once the session is over, offer to chat with anyone who would like to talk further about becoming a Christian.
- Follow up to see how people did with the Accelerate assignment. Don't shame or embarrass anyone who didn't get to the assignment, but honestly challenge them to make this a priority in the coming week.

SESSION 4 — LOVE ME TENDER

- You're now at the halfway point of this study. How is it going? How well is the group connecting? What has been going well and what needs a little work? Are there any adjustments you need to make?
- Don't feel any pressure to get through all the questions. As people open up and talk, don't move on too quickly. Give them space to process what is going on inside them as they engage with this teaching.
- Don't be afraid of silence. When you ask a question, give your group time to think about it. Don't feel like you have to fill every quiet moment with words.
- In this session, Chip will talk about envy and arrogance as barriers to love. This can be a very touchy issue for some because it digs into issues of self-esteem and identity. As you lead the group discussion, don't push people to share if they are uncomfortable doing so.

- If your group is not sharing as much as you would like or if the discussion is being dominated by a person or two, try subgrouping. If your group is 8 people or more, this is a great way to up the level of participation. After watching the video, divide into a couple of smaller groups for the discussion time. It's good to get someone you think would be a good facilitator to volunteer to lead ahead of time.

SESSION 5 — LOOKING FOR LOVE IN ALL THE WRONG PLACES

- Confidentiality is crucial to group life. The moment trust is breached, people will shut down and close up. Mention the importance of confidentiality again this week just to keep it on everyone's radar.

- Each time your group meets, take a few minutes to update on what has happened since the last group meeting. Ask people what they are learning and putting into practice. Remember, being a disciple of Jesus means becoming a "doer of the word".

- Revisit the importance of B.I.O. this week. Reinforce the importance of people integrating these core practices in their lives. For example, talk about the priority of coming before God each day and submitting to the authority of God's truth.

- At the end of the video teaching this week, Chip will ask the group to discuss the question, "Where have you failed in the past and, in your failure, ended up meeting God's love?" This could be an intimidating and uncomfortable question for some people. It would probably be best for you to be prepared to share from your own life first. Your willingness to be vulnerable will give others permission and courage to do the same.

- The final question this week is, "Who is it in your life that needs to hear the words "I believe in you and I'm for you"? As people share their answers, challenge them to make it a point to share this with the people they mentioned.

SESSION 6 — IN THE NAME OF LOVE

- One way to deepen the level of community within your group is to spend time together outside the group meeting. If you haven't already done so, plan something that will allow you to get to know each other better. Also, consider having someone else in the group take responsibility for your fellowship event.

- As you begin this week's session, check to see what people are learning and applying from this study. Don't be afraid to take some time at the beginning of your meeting to review some key ideas from the previous week's lessons.

- Consider asking someone in your group to facilitate next week's lesson. Who knows, there might be a great potential small group leader in your group. It will give you a break and give them a chance to grow.

- This week's session is about misplaced priorities. Chip will talk about the priority of doing life "in community". Question #6 will ask your group to honestly assess how they are doing at building true community with one another. This is a great opportunity to remind the group that true community is more than a meeting and a Bible study. Make sure to leave time for this important question.

SESSION 7 — WHAT THE WORLD NEEDS NOW

- Send an e-mail to each person in your group this week letting them know you prayed for them. Also, let them know that you are grateful that they are in the group.

- Take a few minutes this week before you get into the study to talk about the impact of this study so far. Ask people what they are learning, applying, and changing in their lives. For this study to have lasting impact, it has to be more than just absorbing information. Challenge your group to put what they are learning into action.

- Since this is the next to the last week of this study, you might want to spend some time this week talking about what your group is going to do after you complete this study.

- In this session, Chip will talk about how we find and get love. Question #3 this week asks, "How were you impacted personally by the way your family did or did not express love? How hard is it for you to openly express love?" It's helpful for all of us to have an awareness of how our family experiences have shaped who we are today. Be sure to make time for this question.

SESSION 8 — LOVE TRAIN (GET ON BOARD!)

- Be sure that everyone is clear what your group is doing next after this study.
- In this final session, Chip will talk about sustaining a lifetime of love. One of the ways we sustain a lifetime of love is through the practices of B.I.O. This is a great opportunity to stress these three core elements as crucial for becoming like Jesus.
    - Come "Before God" daily
    - Do life "In Community" weekly
    - Be "On Mission" 24/7
- Question #5 this week will ask, "For you personally, what does it mean to be surrendered to God ("all in")? Is there some area of your life that you are struggling to surrender to God?" Help people in your group understand that surrender is rooted in the goodness and character of God. Surrender is in our best interest and as Chip says, "is the channel through which God's biggest and best blessings flow."
- As this study winds down, this is a good time to plan some kind of party or fellowship after you complete the study. Find the "party person" in your group, and ask them to take on the responsibility of planning a fun experience for the group. Use this party as a time for people to share how God has used this study to grow and change them.

Prayer and Praise

One of the most important things you can do in your group is to pray with and for each other. Write down each other's concerns here so you can remember to pray for these requests during the week.

Use the Follow Up box to record an answer to a prayer or to write down how you might want to follow-up with the person making the request. This could be a phone call, an e-mail or a card. Your personal concern will mean a lot!

DATE	PERSON	PRAYER REQUEST	FOLLOW UP

DATE	PERSON	PRAYER REQUEST	FOLLOW UP

DATE	PERSON	PRAYER REQUEST	FOLLOW UP

DATE	PERSON	PRAYER REQUEST	FOLLOW UP

DATE	PERSON	PRAYER REQUEST	FOLLOW UP

DATE	PERSON	PRAYER REQUEST	FOLLOW UP

DATE	PERSON	PRAYER REQUEST	FOLLOW UP

DATE	PERSON	PRAYER REQUEST	FOLLOW UP

DATE	PERSON	PRAYER REQUEST	FOLLOW UP

DATE	PERSON	PRAYER REQUEST	FOLLOW UP

DATE	PERSON	PRAYER REQUEST	FOLLOW UP

Group Roster

NAME	HOME PHONE	E-MAIL

WHAT'S NEXT?

More Group Studies from Chip Ingram

NEW BIO

Quench Your Thirst for Life

5 video sessions

Cinematic story illustrates Biblical truth in this 5-part video study that unlocks the Biblical DNA for spiritual momentum by examining the questions at the heart of true spirituality.

NEW House or Home Marriage

God's Blueprint for a Great Marriage

10 video sessions

The foundational building blocks of marriage are crumbling before our eyes, and Christians aren't exempt. It's time to go back to the blueprint and examine God's plan for marriages that last for a lifetime.

NEW Good to Great in God's Eyes

10 Practices Great Christians Have in Common

10 video sessions

If you long for spiritual breakthrough, take a closer look at ten powerful practices that will rekindle a fresh infusion of faith and take you from good to great...in God's eyes.

Balancing Life's Demands

Biblical Priorities for Busy Lives

10 video sessions

Busy, tired and stressed out? Learn how to put "first things first" and find peace in the midst of pressure and adversity.

Effective Parenting in a Defective World

Raising Kids that Stand Out from the Crowd

9 video sessions

Packed with examples and advice for raising kids, this series presents Biblical principles for parenting that still work today.

Experiencing God's Dream for Your Marriage

Practical Tools for a Thriving Marriage

12 video sessions

Examine God's design for marriage and the real life tools and practices that will transform it for a lifetime.

Love, Sex & Lasting Relationships

God's Prescription to Enhance Your Love Life

10 video sessions

Do you believe in "true love"? Discover a better way to find love, stay in love, and build intimacy that lasts a lifetime.

The Miracle of Life Change

How to Change for Good

10 video sessions

Ready to make a change? Explore God's process of true transformation and learn to spot barriers that hold you back from receiving God's best.

Overcoming Emotions that Destroy

Constructive Tools for Destructive Emotions

10 video sessions

We all struggle with destructive emotions that can ruin relationships. Learn God's plan to overcome angry feelings for good.

Rebuilding Your Broken World

How God Puts Broken Lives Back Together

8 video sessions

Starting over? Learn how God can reshape your response to trials and bring healing to broken relationships and difficult circumstances.

Why I Believe

Answers to Life's Most Difficult Questions

12 video sessions

Examine the Biblical truth behind the pivotal questions at the heart of human existence and the claims of the Christian faith.

Your Divine Design

Discover, Develop and Deploy Your Spiritual Gifts

8 video sessions

How has God uniquely wired you? Discover God's purpose for spiritual gifts and how to identify your own.

Watch previews & order at www.LivingontheEdge.org